First published in Great Britain 2009 by Dean
an imprint of Egmont UK Limited
239 Kensington High Street,
London W8 6SA

© 2009 Prism Art & Design Limited, a HIT Entertainment company.
The Fireman Sam name and character are trademarks of
Prism Art & Design Limited, a HIT Entertainment company.
Based on an original idea by D Gingell, D Jones and
characters created by RMJ Lee

ISBN 978 0 6035 6445 1
1 3 5 7 9 10 8 6 4 2
Printed in Italy